The Jane Austen Quiz Book

Helen Barton

First published 1997
© Helen Barton 1997

ISBN 0-9527257-1-1

Published by Helen Barton.
Printed by Aspect Design.

For my mother and my sister.

Contents

NAME THE BOOK OR THE CHARACTER

1. There are six famous completed novels by Jane Austen. Name two of them.

2. Only one book is named after its heroine. Do you know which one it is?

3. Which two novels have a one word title?

4. An abbey and a park are found in the titles of two novels. Which ones are they?

5. Do you know the name of the book beginning with this line: "The family of Dashwood had been long settled in Sussex." ?

6. The following are three clergymen. Can you say in which books they appear?
   a) the Rev. Mr Norris   b) Mr Collins
   c) Mr Elton

7. Name the book in which these characters are found: Mr Weston, Harriet Smith, Robert Martin.

8. Of the six completed novels, which was the last to be written?

9. One novel is a satire of the Gothic romances popular in Jane Austen's day but which one is it?

10. Match these characters to the novels in which they are found:
    a) Jane Fairfax   i)   "Sense and Sensibility"
    b) Mr Bingley   ii) "Emma"
    c) Colonel Brandon   iii) "Pride and Prejudice"

11. Name the book which opens with these lines:
    "It is a truth universally acknowledged, that a single man in possession of a good fortune, must be in want of a wife."

12. Which novel's final sentence begins with:
    "She gloried in being a sailor's wife," ?

13. Charles Hayter and Louisa Musgrove appear in "Persuasion". True or false?

14. "Mrs. Thorpe talked chiefly of her children, and Mrs. Allen of her gowns."
    Where does this line come from?

15. "Miss Lucas perceived him from an upper window as he walked towards the house, and instantly set out to meet him accidentally in the lane."
    Where is this from and who is the male character?

16. " 'I have tidings of my harp at last.' "
    Is this from:
    a) "Persuasion"   b) "Emma"
    c) "Mansfield Park" ?

17. Match these characters to the books in which they are found:
    a) Mr Palmer   i) "Emma"
    b) Lady Catherine   ii) "Sense and Sensibility"
       de Bourgh   iii) "Pride and Prejudice"
    c) Miss Bates

18. " 'If there is any thing disagreeable going on, men are always sure to get out of it,' "
    Where is this from?

19. Give the name of the book in which you find these characters:
    Mrs Goddard, "the mistress of a school" and Mr Perry, the apothecary.

20. " 'But people themselves alter so much, that there is something new to be observed in them for ever.' "
    Is this from:
    a) "Sense and Sensibility"   b) "Emma"
    c) "Pride and Prejudice" ?

21. Match these characters to the books in which they are found:
    a) Mrs Norris   i)   "Persuasion"
    b) Mrs Thorpe   ii) "Northanger Abbey"
    c) Mrs Musgrove   iii) "Mansfield Park"

22. "A lady, without a family, was the very best preserver of furniture in the world."
    This is from "Emma". True or false?

23. "she cared for no furniture of a more modern date than the fifteenth century."
    Is this from:
    a) "Mansfield Park"   b) "Northanger Abbey"
    c) "Persuasion" ?

24. "Here she took out her handkerchief; but Elinor did not feel very compassionate."
    Can you say where these lines are found? An extra point if you can also name "she".

25. Name the book from which the following is taken:
    "the sight of Miss Price dripping with wet in the vestibule, was delightful. The value of an event on a wet day in the country was most forcibly brought before her."
    Extra points if you can name the character involved.

26. "A woman, especially, if she have the misfortune of knowing anything, should conceal it as well as she can"
Is this from:
a) "Emma"   b) "Pride and Prejudice"
c) "Northanger Abbey" ?

27. "Friendship is certainly the finest balm for the pangs of disappointed love."
In which novel do you find these lines?

28. The following is from Sense and Sensibility but who are the two characters?
" 'She has done with her son, she has cast him off for ever,' "

29. Lady Dalrymple, Captain Benwick and Captain Harville are all found in the same novel but which one?
Is it:
a) "Emma"   b) "Persuasion"
c) "Mansfield Park" ?

30. Name the book in which the following is found:
"Hollow murmurs seemed to creep along the gallery, and more than once her blood was chilled by the sound of distant moans."

31. "The evening passed with external smoothness, though almost every mind was ruffled."
Is this from "Persuasion" or "Mansfield Park" ?

32. " 'A mother would have been always present; a mother would have been a constant friend; her influence would have been beyond all other.' "
Is this from:
a) "Emma"   b) "Persuasion"
c) "Northanger Abbey" ?

33. The following characters are all found in the same novel. Which one is it?
    Sir John Middleton, Mrs Jennings and John Willoughby.

34. " 'Men have had every advantage of us in telling their own story. Education has been theirs in so much higher a degree; the pen has been in their hands.' "
Can you say where this is from and who is speaking?

35. The following is from "Northanger Abbey". True or false?
    "so with smiles of most exquisite misery, and the laughing eye of utter despondency, she bade her friend adieu, and went on."

36. " 'There are several odd-looking men walking about here, who, I am told, are sailors.' "
Name the novel and an extra point if you can say who is speaking.

HEROINES AND HEROES

1. Three heroines have first names beginning with the letter 'E'. Name as many as you can.

2. Match up the first and second names of the following:
   - a) Elizabeth
   - b) Catherine
   - c) Emma
   - i) Morland
   - ii) Woodhouse
   - iii) Bennet

3. Can you say which heroine belongs to which novel?
   - a) Anne Elliot
   - b) Elinor Dashwood
   - c) Elizabeth Bennet
   - i) "Pride and Prejudice"
   - ii) "Sense and Sensibility"
   - iii) "Persuasion"

4. "sense will always have attractions for me."
   Who says this?

5. One heroine is particularly keen on match making. Who is she?

6. "No one who had ever seen Catherine Morland in her infancy would have supposed her born to be an heroine."
   These are the opening lines of which novel?

7. "for she had a lively, playful disposition, which delighted in anything ridiculous."
   Do these lines describe:
   - a) Elizabeth Bennet   b) Emma Woodhouse
   - c) Fanny Price ?

8. Match these heroes to their novels:
   - a) Mr Knightley
   - b) Edmund Bertram
   - c) Henry Tilney
   - i) "Northanger Abbey"
   - ii) "Emma"
   - iii) "Mansfield Park"

9. In "Sense and Sensibility" who is said to be:
   "not handsome, and his manners required intimacy to make them pleasing." ?

10. Who is
"one of the few people who could see faults in Emma Woodhouse, and the only one who ever told her of them;" ?

11. The following describes a hero but which one?
"He was at the same time haughty, reserved, and fastidious, and his manners, though well bred, were not inviting."

12. "Few young ladies of eighteen could be less called on to speak their opinion than......."
Who? Is it:
a) Fanny Price   b) Catherine Morland
c) Elizabeth Bennet ?

13. Can you name the novels in which the following heroines are found?
a) Emma Woodhouse   b) Fanny Price
c) Catherine Morland

14. Match these heroes and heroines:
a) Edward Ferrars   i)   Elizabeth Bennet
b) Captain Wentworth   ii) Elinor Dashwood
c) Mr Darcy   iii) Anne Elliot

15. Which heroine does this refer to:
"She had given him up to oblige others. It had been the effect of over-persuasion." ?

16. " 'I suppose I am graver than other people.' "
Here the heroine is talking about herself and here she is described as a child of ten:
"exceedingly timid and shy, and shrinking from notice;"
Who is she?

17. Which heroine finds in a cabinet a manuscript which turns out to be an "inventory of linen." Is it:
    a) Catherine Morland   b) Elizabeth Bennet
    c) Anne Elliot ?

18.   "She had an excellent heart; her disposition was affectionate, and her feelings were strong: but she knew how to govern them:"
This describes Elinor Dashwood. True or false?

19.   " 'I have very little to say for my own conduct - I was tempted by his attentions, and allowed myself to appear pleased.' "
Who says this? Is it:
    a) Elizabeth Bennet   b) Anne Elliot
    c) Emma Woodhouse ?

20. "I am going to take a heroine whom no one but myself will much like," said Jane Austen. Who is she?

21. Name the hero who says:
    " 'I never wish to offend, but I am so foolishly shy, that I often seem negligent, when I am only kept back by my natural awkwardness.' "
Is it:
    a) Henry Tilney   b) Mr Darcy
    c) Edward Ferrars ?

22.   " 'If I loved you less, I might be able to talk about it more.' "
Who is speaking and to whom?

23. The following are names of three heroes. Match up first and second names:
    a) Henry   i)   Wentworth
    b) Frederick   ii) Ferrars
    c) Edward   iii) Tilney.

24. " 'There is a stubbornness about me that never can bear to be frightened at the will of others. My courage always rises with every attempt to intimidate me.' "
This is Elizabeth Bennet describing herself. True or false?

25. Do you know Mr Darcy's first name?

26. "Her passion for ancient edifices was next in degree to her passion for .....".
Where is this taken from and to whom do the lines refer?

27. Which heroine's father says to her:
" 'Are your out of your senses, to be accepting this man? Have not you always hated him?' "

28. Match these heroines to their heroes:
   a) Emma Woodhouse   i) Henry Tilney
   b) Fanny Price   ii) Edmund Bertram
   c) Catherine Morland   iii) Mr Knightley

29. The following both describe the same heroine and hero. Who are they?
"they were neither of them quite enough in love to think that three hundred and fifty pounds a year would supply them with the comforts of life."
and :
"They had in fact nothing to wish for, but the marriage of Colonel Brandon and Marianne, and rather better pasturage for their cows."

30. "they were divided only by Mrs. Musgrove. It was no insignificant barrier indeed."
Who are they?

31. Which heroine is said to have been
    " a very pretty girl, but her bloom had vanished early;"
    Is it:
    a) Catherine Morland   b) Elinor Dashwood
    c) Anne Elliot ?

32.   " 'He is not a gallant man, but he is a very humane one;' "
    Which heroine is talking about which hero?

33. The following refers to Fanny Price in "Mansfield Park". True or false?
    "But my affair is widely different; I bring back my heroine to her home in solitude and disgrace,"

34. "he talked no nonsense; he paid no compliments;" and his name is said to be one of "heroism and renown;"
    Who is he? Choose from:
    a) Captain Wentworth   b) Edmund Bertram
    c) Henry Tilney

35. Do you know the name of the hero who writes a letter to the heroine in which he says:
    "I have loved none but you."
    and
    "A word, a look, will be enough to decide whether I enter your father's house this evening or never." ?

36. Name the heroine who, as a young girl, is described as follows:
    "She was fond of all boys' plays, and greatly preferred cricket,"
    and
    "from fifteen to seventeen she was in training for a heroine;"

LOVE AND MARRIAGE

1. Who does Elizabeth Bennet marry in "Pride and Prejudice"?

2. In "Emma" who marries Mr Knightley ?

3. Match these two Bennet sisters to their husbands:
   a) Jane   i)   Mr Wickham
   b) Lydia   ii)   Mr Bingley

4.   "Husbands and wives generally understand when opposition will be vain."
   Is this from:
   a) "Sense and Sensibility"   b) "Persuasion"
   c) "Northanger Abbey" ?

5. Who in "Sense and Sensibility" could "never love by halves" but marries a man who "still sought the constitutional safeguard of a flannel waistcoat!" ?

6. In "Persuasion" Anne Elliot marries a Captain but is it Captain Benwick or Captain Wentworth?

7. The following characters from "Emma" either marry or are engaged to be married but can you name their partners?
   a) Frank Churchill   b) Harriet Smith
   c) Mr Elton

8.   "The business of her life was to get her daughters married;"
   Where is this from and to whom does it refer ?

9.   "Henry and Catherine were married, the bells rang and everybody smiled;"
   Is this from:
   a) "Northanger Abbey"   b) "Persuasion"
   c) "Mansfield Park" ?

LOVE AND MARRIAGE

10. " 'Happiness in marriage is entirely a matter of chance.' "
This is from "Pride and Prejudice" but do you know who says it? Is it:
a) Elizabeth   b) Mr Darcy
c) Charlotte Lucas ?

11. At the end of "Persuasion" the Musgrove sisters are both engaged to be married but to whom? Match up the right names.
a) Henrietta   i) Captain Benwick
b) Louisa   ii) Charles Hayter

12. In "Mansfield Park" there are three Ward sisters. Can you say who each of them marries?

13. Name the person Mr Collins marries in "Pride and Prejudice".

14. "The wedding was very much like other weddings, where the parties have no taste for finery or parade;"
This describes Emma's wedding. True or false?

15. " 'I consider a country-dance as an emblem of marriage. Fidelity and complaisance are the principal duties of both;' "
This is from "Northanger Abbey" but who says it?

16. Can you say where the following is from?
"It was a very proper wedding. The bride was elegantly dressed; the two bridesmaids were duly inferior; her father gave her away; her mother stood with salts in her hand, expecting to be agitated; her aunt tried to cry; and the service was impressively read by Dr Grant."

17. Lucy Steele is a character from "Sense and Sensibility" who is involved with the two Ferrars brothers. Who is she
    a) first engaged to;   b) later married to ?

18. This is from "Persuasion" but can you name the three characters involved:
    "They were more in love with him; yet there it was not love. It was a little fever of admiration; but it might, probably must, end in love with some." ?

19.   " 'What are men to rocks and mountains? ' "
    Who says it? Is it:
    a) Elizabeth Bennet   b) Emma Woodhouse
    c) Catherine Morland ?

20.   "Without thinking highly either of men or of matrimony, marriage had always been her object; it was the only honourable provision for well-educated young women of small fortune, and however uncertain of giving happiness, must be their pleasantest preservative from want."
    This is from "Pride and Prejudice" but who is the character? Is it:
    a) Charlotte Lucas   b) Caroline Bingley
    c) Lydia Bennet ?

21. Mr Rushworth ("Mansfield Park") marries one of the Bertram sisters but which one? Is it:
    a) Julia   b) Maria ?

22. Name the character from "Emma" who is described as being:
    "one of those, who, having once begun, would be always in love."

23.   " 'Oh, Lizzy! do anything rather than marry without affection.' "
    Where is this from and who is speaking ?

LOVE AND MARRIAGE

24. In "Northanger Abbey" the man Eleanor Tilney marries is un-named. True or false?

25. John Willoughby ("Sense and Sensibility") marries but what is the name of his wife? Is it:
    a) Sophia Grey   b) Lucy Steele
    c) Marianne Dashwood ?

26.   " 'He has no occasion to marry, either to fill up his time or his heart.' "
    Mrs Weston is talking here of Frank Churchill. True or false?

27.   "The acknowledged lovers talked and laughed, the unacknowledged were silent."
    These lines are from "Pride and Prejudice" but can you name the four lovers?

28.   "Who can be in doubt of what followed? When any two young people take it into their heads to marry, they are pretty sure by perseverance to carry their point, be they ever so poor, or ever so imprudent,"
    Is this from:
    a) "Emma"   b) "Northanger Abbey"
    c) "Persuasion" ?

29. Which character from "Mansfield Park" says: "Matrimony was her object, provided she could marry well:" ?

30. Name the person who has "very little intention of every marrying at all" and says:
    " 'A woman is not to marry a man merely because she is asked, or because he is attached to her, and can write a tolerable letter.' "

SISTERS AND BROTHERS

1. How many Bennet sisters are there in "Pride and Prejudice":
   a) Three   b) Five   c) Seven ?

2. Name as many of them as you can.

3. Match these sisters with the books in which they appear:
   a) The Dashwood sisters   i) "Persuasion";
   b) The Bertram sisters   ii) "Mansfield Park"
   c) The Musgrove sisters   iii) "Sense and Sensibility"

4. Mr Darcy in "Pride and Prejudice" has a sister. What is her name?

5. In "Emma" who has a sister called Isabella?

6. "beware how you give your heart."
   This is from "Northanger Abbey" but can you name the brother who writes it to his sister?

7. In "Sense and Sensibility" there are two Dashwood sisters. True or false?

8. Mary Crawford and her brother Henry are characters in "Mansfield Park". True or false?

9. Can you give the names of the two Steele sisters who appear in "Sense and Sensibility" ?

10. "Mrs. Musgrove and Mrs. Hayter were sisters".
    Where is this line taken from?

11. " 'Had I died, in what peculiar misery should I have left you, my nurse, my friend, my sister! - You, who had seen all the fretful selfishness of my latter days; who had known all the murmurings of my heart!' "
    Can you say who is talking to her sister?

12. The Elliot sisters are characters in "Northanger Abbey". True or false?

13. These are the closing lines of one of the novels but which one is it?
    "let it not be ranked as the least considerable, that though sisters, and living almost within sight of each other, they could live without disagreement between themselves, or producing coolness between their husbands."

14. In "Emma" Mr Knightley has a brother. True or false?

15. How many sisters does Anne Elliot have in "Persuasion"? Is it one or two?

16. " 'What strange creatures brothers are!' "
    This is from "Mansfield Park" but who says it? Is it:
    a) Mrs Norris   b) Julia Bertram
    c) Mary Crawford ?

17. The following are both from the same book but which one?
    "The sisters, handsome, clever, and encouraging, were an amusement to his sated mind;"
    and
    "Each sister believed herself the favourite."
    Is it:
    a) "Mansfield Park"   b) "Persuasion"
    c) "Pride and Prejudice" ?

18. Two of Mr Bingley's sisters appear in "Pride and Prejudice". Can you name them ?

19. James Morland and John Thorpe are characters in "Northanger Abbey". Both have sisters who are main characters in the book. A point for each one you can name.

20. Anne Elliot and Elinor Dashwood have two sisters each. Who belongs to who?
    a) Anne Elliot   i) Marianne and Margaret
    b) Elinor Dashwood   ii) Elizabeth and Mary.

21. Name the two grown up sisters of Charles Musgrove in "Persuasion".

22. Which Bennet sister is described as:
    "untamed, unabashed, wild, noisy, and fearless."
    Is it:
    a) Lydia   b) Kitty   c) Mary

23.   "Mary was not so repulsive and unsisterly as Elizabeth,"
    Is this from:
    a) "Pride and Prejudice"   b) "Persuasion"
    c) "Emma" ?

24. In which book do two sisters marry two brothers?

25. Edward Ferrars in "Sense and Sensibility" has a brother. What is his name?

26. In "Mansfield Park" William is Fanny's favourite brother. True or false?

27. Which heroine has brothers called Sam and Tom and which hero has a sister called Eleanor?

SETTINGS

1. Which heroine lives at Hartfield?

2. Longbourn and Netherfield Park are settings in "Pride and Prejudice." True or false?

3. Bath is a setting in which two novels?

4. The following are all found in "Sense and Sensibility". Match them up with the people who live there:
   - a) Combe Magna   i) Colonel Brandon
   - b) Delaford   ii) The Palmers
   - c) Cleveland   iii) John Willoughby

5. Where would you find Kellynch Hall? Is it in:
   - a) "Mansfield Park"   b) "Northanger Abbey"
   - c) "Persuasion" ?

6. Who has a house called Pemberley?

7. In "Persuasion" where does Louisa Musgrove fall and hurt her head?

8. In "Mansfield Park" which place does Fanny Price leave to go and live with her relatives, the Bertrams?

9. Randalls, Donwell and Abbey-Mill-Farm are all found in "Emma" but who lives where? Match up the people with the places where they live.
   - a) Mr Knightley   b) Robert Martin
   - c) Mr and Mrs Weston

10. Name the character in "Pride and Prejudice" who lives at Rosings.

11. "The whole building enclosed a large court, and two sides of the quadrangle, rich in Gothic ornaments, stood forward for admiration."
Can you name the book from which these lines are taken?

12. Which heroine dislikes Bath, having spent three years at school there?

13. Match these settings to their novels:
    a) Highbury   i) "Mansfield Park"
    b) Uppercross   ii) "Emma"
    c) Sotherton   iii) "Persuasion"

14. In "Emma", where is it that Frank Churchill and Jane Fairfax first meet? Is it:
    a) Enscombe   b) Highbury
    c) Weymouth ?

15. Which novel has Norland in Sussex and Barton Cottage in Devonshire as settings?

16. This is from "Pride and Prejudice" but where is the place?
    "a situation of such double danger as a watering place and a camp."

17. Which family live in a Wiltshire village called Fullerton? Is it:
    a) The Morlands in "Northanger Abbey"
    b) The Bertrams in "Mansfield Park" ?

18. Name the novel from which the following lines are taken:
    "Its long, damp passages, its narrow cells and ruined chapel, were to be within her daily reach, and she could not entirely subdue the hope of some traditional legends, some awful memorials of an injured and ill-fated nun."

19. The following is a description from "Mansfield Park" but can you name the house to which the garden belongs?
    "The lawn, bounded on each side by a high wall, contained beyond the first planted area a bowling-green, and beyond the bowling-green a long terrace walk,"

20. Name the novel where the hero and heroine walk round Beechen Cliff. Is it:
    a) "Persuasion"   b) "Emma"
    c) "Northanger Abbey" ?

21. "But still, there certainly were a dreadful multitude of ugly women in Bath; and as for the men! they were infinitely worse."
    These lines are from "Persuasion". True or false?

PRIDE AND PREJUDICE

1. Who is the eldest of the Bennet girls and who is the youngest?

2. "She was a woman of mean understanding, little information, and uncertain temper."
Name the character.

3. Elizabeth has a close friend. What is her name?

4. Mr Bennet is related to Mr Collins but in what way?

5. Mr Collins has a patron. Do you know her name?

6. Which of the Bennet sisters is "the only plain one in the family" and is, at the end of the book, "the only daughter who remained at home;" ?

7. Mrs Bennet has a sister and a brother. Can you name either or both?

8. Who
"began directly to calculate with more interest than the matter had ever excited before, how many years longer Mr Bennet was likely to live;" ?
Is it:
   a) Lady Lucas   b) Lady Catherine
   c) Sir William ?

9. "His appearance was greatly in his favour; he had all the best part of beauty, a fine countenance, a good figure, and very pleasing address."
This describes Mr Darcy. True or false?

10. Who does Elizabeth describe as:
    " 'a conceited, pompous, narrow-minded, silly man;' "
    and who is she talking to when she says:
    " 'We are each of an unsocial, taciturn disposition, unwilling to speak, unless we expect to say something that will amaze the whole room,' " ?

11. "He was storing his memory with anecdotes and noble names."
    Who is this? Is it:
    a) Mr Collins   b) Sir William Lucas ?

12. Who says:
    " 'My daughter and my nephew are formed for each other.' " ?
    Is it:
    a) Mrs Bennet   b) Lady Lucas
    c) Lady Catherine ?

13. "for jealousy had not yet made her desperate,"
    Is this:
    a) Charlotte Lucas   b) Lydia Bennet
    c) Miss Bingley ?

14. Which character is described as:
    "a tall, large woman, with strongly-marked features, which might once have been handsome." ?

15. Who invites Lydia to Brighton?

16. "He was fond of the country and of books; and from these tastes had arisen his principal enjoyments. To his wife, he was very little otherwise indebted, than as her ignorance and folly had contributed to his amusement."
    Can you name the married couple described in these lines?

17. "his style was not penitent, but haughty. It was all pride and insolence."
Who is this?

18. Jane Bennet says:
" 'The more I see of the world, the more am I dissatisfied with it;' "
True or false?

19. Elizabeth goes on holiday with the Gardiners. Which county do they visit?

20. Mr Darcy has a housekeeper at Pemberley. Do you know her name?

21. Which of the Bennet girls is described as:
"weak-spirited, irritable, and completely under Lydia's guidance," ?

22. One of Elizabeth's sisters elopes with Wickham. Which one is it?

23. Name the Bennet sister who says:
" 'This is a most unfortunate affair; and will probably be much talked of. But we must stem the tide of malice, and pour into the wounded bosoms of each other, the balm of sisterly consolation.' "

24. " 'and her nieces are very pretty behaved girls, and not at all handsome: I like them prodigiously.' "
This is Lady Catherine talking. True or false?

25. George Wickham "will never marry a woman without some money. He cannot afford it." True or false?

EMMA

1. "Emma" begins with a wedding but whose is it?

2. Who is
   "a man of unexceptionable character, easy fortune, suitable age and pleasant manners;" ?
   Is it:
   a) Mr Weston   b) Mr Knightley
   c) Mr Elton ?

3. What relation is Frank Churchill to Mr Weston?

4. "He was a nervous man, easily depressed; fond of every body that he was used to, and hating to part with them; hating change of every kind."
   Who do these lines describe?

5. Can you name Emma's ex-governess and friend?

6. Isabella and John Knightley have five children. Name as many as you can.

7. "His gallantry was always on the alert".
   Who is this?

8. Who proposes marriage to Emma in a carriage?

9. "The simplicity and cheerfulness of her nature, her contented and grateful spirit, were a recommendation to every body and a mine of felicity to herself."
   Which character is described here?

10. Jane Fairfax is related to Miss Bates but in what way?

11. "She was a very pretty girl, and her beauty happened to be of a sort which Emma particularly admired."
    This is a description of Jane Fairfax. True or false?

12. Emma dissuades Harriet Smith from marrying the man she loves and suggests someone else. Can you name the two men?

13. Emma and Mr Knightley are talking of the same person. Who is he?
Emma: " 'He will be a completely gross, vulgar farmer' "
Mr Knightley: " 'He always speaks to the purpose; open, straight forward, and very well judging.' "

14. Name the character who is an orphan and who has been living with the Campbell family.

15. "but their straight-forward emotions left no room for the little zigzags of embarrassment."
Who are these two characters?

16. Can you say which character has a piano anonymously delivered to her?

17. What is the name of the "principal woollen-draper, linen-draper, and haberdasher's shop" ?

18. Name the character who had "gone off to London, merely to have his hair cut." Is it:
    a) Mr Elton   b) Frank Churchill
    c) Mr Knightley ?

19. " 'Open the windows! - but surely, Mr Churchill, nobody would think of opening the windows at Randalls. Nobody could be so imprudent! I never heard of such a thing. Dancing with open windows!' "
This is Mr Woodhouse. True or false.

20. The following three characters are all talking about the same person but who says what?
    a) " 'I quite rave about Jane Fairfax.' "
    b) " 'Jane Fairfax is a very charming young woman - but not even Jane Fairfax is perfect.' "
    c) " 'I wish Jane Fairfax very well; but she tires me to death.' "
    i) Emma   ii) Mrs Elton   iii) Mr Knightley.

21.   " 'Surprizes are foolish things. The pleasure is not enhanced, and the inconvenience is often considerable.' "
Mr Woodhouse is speaking here. True or false?

22. Who is "as elegant as lace and pearls could make her," ? Is it:
    a) Harriet Smith   b) Mrs Elton
    c) Miss Bates ?

23. Emma and Mr Knightley are both talking about the same character but who is he?
    Emma: " ' I should not like a man who is so soon discomposed by a hot morning.' "
    Mr Knightley: " 'He is a disgrace to the name of man.' "

24. Someone is described by Emma as an
    " 'Insufferable woman!' "
    and
    " 'A little upstart, vulgar being,' "
    but who is it? Is it:
    a) Mrs Elton   b) Miss Bates
    c) Jane Fairfax ?

25. Which character says:
    " 'They came from Birmingham, which is not a place to promise much,' "
    and
    " 'She always travels with her own sheets; an excellent precaution.' "

26. Emma has only once called Mr Knightley by a Christian name but what is it? Is it:
    a) George   b) John   c) Henry ?

27. Who at the end of "Emma" gives birth to a baby daughter?

SENSE AND SENSIBILITY

1. The Dashwood sisters have a half brother. What is his name?

2. Who is said to be "a strong caricature" of her husband, being "more narrow-minded and selfish." ?

3.   " 'people always live for ever when there is any annuity to be paid them;' "
Who says this? Is it:
   a) John Dashwood   b) Fanny Dashwood
   c) Marianne ?

4. A relation of Mrs Dashwood offers her Barton Cottage. What is his name?

5.   "Her manners had all the elegance which her husband's wanted. But they would have been improved by some share of his frankness and warmth;"
Can you name the couple referred to here?

6. The following describes Colonel Brandon. True or false?
   "He was silent and grave. His appearance, however, was not unpleasing, in spite of his being, in the opinion of Marianne and Margaret, an absolute old bachelor, for he was on the wrong side of five-and-thirty."

7. What is the name of Mrs Middleton's mother?

8. Name the character who is described as:
   "a good-humoured, merry, fat, elderly woman, who talked a great deal, seemed very happy, and rather vulgar."

9. Which Dashwood sister twists her foot in a fall and who carries her home?

10. "He was exactly formed to engage Marianne's heart;" Name the character.

11.   " 'I could not be happy with a man whose taste did not in every point coincide with my own.' "
Is this Elinor or Marianne talking?

12.   " 'Know your own happiness. You want nothing but patience - or give it a more fascinating name, call it hope.' "
Mrs Dashwood is speaking here but who is she talking to? Is it:
    a) Elinor   b) Marianne
    c) Edward ?

13. For one point, name the character who is speaking; for another, say who he is talking about.
    " 'But he is a pleasant, good-humoured fellow, and has got the nicest little black bitch of a pointer I ever saw.' "

14. Mrs Jennings has two daughters. One is Lady Middleton. Who is the other ?

15.   "he hardly ever falls in love with anybody."
This is Mrs Palmer talking but about whom? Is it:
    a) Colonel Brandon   b) Willougby
    c) Edward Ferrars ?

16. Edward Ferrars is related to Fanny Dashwood but in what way?

17. " 'My love, you contradict everybody,' " said his wife, with her usual laugh. " 'Do you know that you are quite rude?' " Name this couple.

18.   "contenting herself with merely giving her husband a gentle reprimand on the subject five or six times every day."
Do you know the names of the married couple here?

19. Who is the husband of "a very silly woman"?

20. Can you name the character who is described as: "naturally clever...but her powers had received no aid from education," ?

21. Mrs Palmer invites Elinor and Marianne to stay in London. True or false?

22. What is the name of the woman Colonel Brandon was once in love with?

23. Eliza has a daughter. Do you know the name of the man who seduces her?

24. "a little, thin woman, upright, even to formality, in her figure, and serious, even to sourness, in her aspect."
Is this:
    a) Mrs Ferrars   b) Mrs Palmer
    c) Fanny Dashwood ?

25. "her folly, though evident, was not disgusting because it was not conceited; and Elinor could have forgiven everything but her laugh."
This is Mrs Palmer. True or false?

26. Elinor is talking here but to whom?
    "You have proved yourself, on the whole, less faulty than I had believed you. You have proved your heart less wicked, much less wicked."

PERSUASION

1. "Vanity was the beginning and end" of whose character?

2. Lady Elliot, Anne's mother, had a close friend. What is her name?

3. Who is "a civil, cautious lawyer." ?

4. Whose daughter is Mrs Clay?

5. Can you name the tenants of Kellynch Hall?

6. "a sailor grows old sooner than any other man;" Who says this?

7. Mrs Croft is related to Captain Wentworth. Is she:
   a) his cousin   b) his aunt
   c) his sister ?

8. Who has "freckles, and a projecting tooth, and a clumsy wrist,"? Is it:
   a) Mrs Clay   b) Mrs Croft
   c) Lady Russell?

9. What is "the Laconia"?

10. " 'no ship, under my command, shall ever convey a family of ladies any where, if I can help it.' "
Admiral Croft says this. True or false?

11. Name the character who says to her brother:
   " 'But I hate to hear you talking so, like a fine gentleman, and as if women were all fine ladies, instead of rational creatures. We none of us expect to be in smooth water all our days.' "

12.   " 'I always look upon her as able to persuade a person to any thing!' "
Henrietta Musgrove is talking but about whom? Is it:
   a) Lady Russell   b) Mrs Clay
   c) Elizabeth Elliot ?

13. Captain Wentworth has friends in Lyme. What are they called?

14. Mary, Anne's sister, has two sons. One is named after her husband, the other after her father. What are they called?

15. Who now lives with the Harvilles and was engaged to Captain Harville's sister?

16. Give the name of Captain Harville's sister and say what happened to her.

17. Anne meets a former school friend in Bath but what is her name?

18.   " 'You need not tell her so, but I thought her dress hideous the other night. I used to think she had some taste in dress, but I was ashamed of her at the concert. ' "
Elizabeth Elliot is talking here but about whom?

19. Lady Russell is the subject of the following but who is talking this time?
   " 'Morning visits are never fair by women at her time of life, who make themselves up so little. If she would only wear rouge, she would not be afraid of being seen;' "

MANSFIELD PARK

1. In which county is Mansfield Park?

2. What age is Fanny Price when she comes to live with the Bertrams? Is she:
   a) Eight   b) Ten   c) Twelve ?

3. Lady Bertram and Mrs Norris are both related to Fanny but in what way?

4. Fanny has four cousins, two boys and two girls. True or false?

5. How many of them can you name? A point for each one.

6. William, is Fanny's favourite brother. What does he become?

7. Whom does the following line describe:
   "her love of money was equal to her love of directing," ?

8.   "he recommended the books which charmed her leisure hours, he encouraged her taste, and corrected her judgement:"
   Name the two characters referred to in these lines.

9.   "She was a woman who spent her days in sitting, nicely dressed, on a sopha, doing some long piece of needlework, of little use and no beauty, thinking more of her pug than her children,"
   Who is this?

10. Which character is described as being:
    "a heavy young man, with not more than common sense;" ?
    Is it:
    a) Mr Rushworth   b) Tom Bertram
    c) Henry Crawford ?

11. Mary and Henry Crawford are related to Mrs Grant but in what way?

12. " 'Give a girl an education, and introduce her properly into the world, and ten to one but she has the means of settling well, without farther expense to anybody.' "
Who is talking? Is it:
   a) Sir Thomas   b) Lady Bertram
   c) Mrs Norris ?

13. "To the education of her daughters" who "paid not the smallest attention. She had not time for such cares." ?

14. Sir Thomas Bertram has an estate in Antigua. True or False?

15. Which one of Fanny's cousins gives her an "old grey pony"?

16. "Active and fearless, and, though rather small, strongly made, she seemed formed for a horsewoman;"
Is this:
   a) Fanny Price   b) Maria Bertram
   c) Mary Crawford ?

17. The following both describe the same character. Can you name her?
   "she burst through his recital with the proposal of soup."
and
   "was now trying to be in a bustle without having anything to bustle about,"

18. Mary Crawford says:
     " ' A large income is the best recipe for happiness I ever heard of.' "
     True or false?

19. Who says:
     " 'My intentions are only not to be poor.' "
     Is it:
     a) Henry Crawford   b) Edmund Bertram
     c) Julia Bertram ?

20.   " 'A woman can never be too fine while she is all in white.' "
     Who says this?

21.   " 'my plan is to make Fanny Price in love with me. ' "
     This is Tom Bertram talking. True or false?

22.   " 'I - I cannot like him, sir, well enough to marry him.' "
     This is Fanny speaking but can you say who she is talking to and name the person she is talking about?

23. Whose home is described as:
     "the abode of noise, disorder, and impropriety." ?

24. Which one of Fanny's cousins leaves her husband for the "well-known and captivating Mr C.," and who is Mr C?

25. Who does Julia Bertram elope with?

26. When Fanny returns to Mansfield Park, which sister does she take with her?

27. Name the character who dies after "three great institutionary dinners in one week,".

NORTHANGER ABBEY

1. What profession is Catherine Morland's father?

2. Do you know his first name?

3.   "She had neither beauty, genius, accomplishment nor manner." and "Dress was her passion."
   Both describe the same character. Who is she?

4. Catherine comes from a large family. How many brothers and sisters does she have? Is it:
   a) Seven   b) Nine   c) Eleven ?

5. Mrs Thorpe invites Catherine to Bath. True or false?

6. Whom do the following lines describe?:
   "He seemed to be about four or five and twenty, was rather tall, had a pleasing countenance, a very intelligent and lively eye, and, if not quite handsome, was very near it."

7. What is Henry Tilney's profession?

8. Name the street in Bath where the Allens and Catherine stay?

9. How do Mrs Thorpe and Mrs Allen know one another?

10.   "He was a stout young man, of middling height,"
    Does this describe John Thorpe or James Morland?

11.   " 'Novels are all so full of nonsense and stuff!' "
    Who says this?

12.   " 'These schemes are not at all the thing. Young men and women driving about the country in open carriages! Now and then it is very well; but going to inns and public places together! It is not right;' "
    Mr Allen says this to Catherine. True or false?

13. Henry Tilney has a brother. What is his name? Is it:
   a) Charles   b) William
   c) Frederick ?

14. Who says:
   " 'Open carriages are nasty things. A clean gown is not five minutes' wear in them. You are splashed getting in and getting out; and the wind takes your hair and your bonnet in every direction." ?

15. Mrs Allen has sons called John, William and Edward. True or false?

16. Name the person who speaks the following lines. An extra point if you know who he is speaking to.
   " 'no one can think more highly of the understanding of women than I do. In my opinion, nature has given them so much that they never find it necessary to use more than half.' "

17. " 'I never think of myself.' " and " 'I hate money;'" Who says this? Is it:
   a) Mrs Thorpe   b) Isabella
   c) Mrs Allen ?

18. Henry Tilney has a parsonage in a village starting with the letter 'W'. What is the name of the village?

19. " 'A little harmless flirtation or so will occur, and one is often drawn on to give more encouragement than one wishes to stand by.' "
   Who is speaking and to whom?

20. Name the character who says:

> " 'No man is offended by another man's admiration of the woman he loves; it is the woman only who can make it a torment.' "

Is it:
a) Henry Tilney   b) James Morland
c) General Tilney ?

21. Who had "no leisure for speech, being at once blushing, tying her gown, and forming wise resolutions with the most violent despatch."?

Is it:
a) Catherine   b) Eleanor Tilney
c) Isabella ?

22. Can you name the character who is described as "a vain coquette" and who says:

> " 'I wear nothing but purple now: I know I look hideous in it, but no matter;' " ?

23. Whose mother says

> " 'You have had a long run of amusement, and now you must try to be useful.' " ?

DIFFICULT ONES

1. When and where was Jane Austen born?

2. What is the Juvenilia?

3. Can you name Jane Austen's only sister?

4. In what form is "Lady Susan" written?

5. "Northanger Abbey" was first written under what title?

6. How old was Jane Austen when she began "Volume the First"?

7. Name the novel written in the form of letters in 1795 and given the title of its two heroines' names.

8. "Emma" was begun in January 1814. When was it finished?

9. What was the profession of Jane Austen's paternal grandfather?

10. "First Impressions" was begun in 1796. What is it subsequently known as?

11. Do you know the name of Jane Austen's oldest brother?

12. How old was Jane Austen when she completed "Love and Freindship"?

13. Name the work prefaced by the author's line: "N B There will be very few Dates in this History".

14. Which of Jane Austen's works was begun in the year of her death and remains unfinished?

15. Where would you find a character called Miss Margaret Lesley?

16. In which unfinished work are the Parkers and Denhams found?

17. Where and when did Jane Austen die?

18. Two novels were published posthumously. Can you name them both ?

ANSWERS: NAME THE BOOK OR THE CHARACTER

1. "Pride and Prejudice", "Emma", "Sense and Sensibility", "Northanger Abbey", "Mansfield Park" and "Persuasion".

2. "Emma".

3. "Emma" and "Persuasion".

4. "Northanger Abbey" and "Mansfield Park".

5. "Sense and Sensibility".

6. a) the Rev. Mr Norris : "Mansfield Park"
   b) Mr Collins   : "Pride and Prejudice"
   c) Mr Elton   : "Emma"

7. "Emma".

8. "Persuasion".

9. "Northanger Abbey".

10. a) Jane Fairfax   : ii) "Emma"
    b) Mr Bingley   : iii) "Pride and Prejudice"
    c) Colonel Brandon : i) "Sense and Sensibility".

11. "Pride and Prejudice".

12. "Persuasion".

13. True.

14. "Northanger Abbey".

15. "Pride and Prejudice." Mr Collins.

16. c) "Mansfield Park".

17. a) Mr Palmer   : ii) "Sense and Sensibility"
    b) Lady Catherine : iii) "Pride and Prejudice"
    c) Miss Bates   : i) "Emma".

ANSWERS: NAME THE BOOK OR THE CHARACTER

18. "Persuasion".

19. "Emma".

20. c) "Pride and Prejudice".

21. a) Mrs Norris   : iii) "Mansfield Park"
    b) Mrs Thorpe   : ii) "Northanger Abbey"
    c) Mrs Musgrove   : i) "Persuasion".

22. False. "Persuasion".

23. b) "Northanger Abbey" .

24. "Sense and Sensibility". Lucy Steele.

25. "Mansfield Park". Mary Crawford.

26. c) "Northanger Abbey".

27. "Northanger Abbey".

28. Mrs Ferrars and Edward Ferrars.

29. b) "Persuasion".

30. "Northanger Abbey".

31. "Mansfield Park".

32. c) "Northanger Abbey".

33. "Sense and Sensibility".

34. "Persuasion". Anne Elliot.

35. True.

36. "Persuasion". Elizabeth Elliot.

1. Elizabeth, Emma and Elinor.

2. Elizabeth Bennet, Catherine Morland, Emma Woodhouse.

3. Anne Elliot - "Persuasion"; Elinor Dashwood - "Sense and Sensibility"; Elizabeth Bennet - "Pride and Prejudice".

4. Elinor Dashwood.

5. Emma.

6. "Northanger Abbey".

7. a) Elizabeth Bennet.

8. a) Mr Knightley   - ii) "Emma"
   b) Edmund Bertram   - iii) "Mansfield Park"
   c) Henry Tilney   - i) "Northanger Abbey"

9. Edward Ferrars.

10. Mr Knightley.

11. Mr Darcy.

12. a) Fanny Price.

13. a) "Emma" b) "Mansfield Park"
    c) "Northanger Abbey"

14. Edward Ferrars and Elinor Dashwood; Captain Wentworth and Anne Elliot; Mr Darcy and Elizabeth Bennet.

15. Anne Elliot.

16. Fanny Price.

17. a) Catherine Morland.

ANSWERS: HEROINES AND HEROES

18. True.

19. c) Emma Woodhouse.

20. Emma.

21. c) Edward Ferrars.

22. Mr Knightley to Emma.

23. Henry Tilney; Frederick Wentworth; Edward Ferrars.

24. True.

25. Fitzwilliam.

26. "Northanger Abbey". Catherine Morland and Henry Tilney.

27. Elizabeth Bennet's.

28. Emma and Mr Knightley; Fanny Price and Edmund Bertram; Catherine Morland and Henry Tilney.

29. Elinor Dashwood and Edward Ferrars.

30. Anne Elliot and Captain Wentworth.

31. c) Anne Elliot.

32. Emma about Mr Knightley.

33. False. Catherine Morland in "Northanger Abbey".

34. b) Edmund Bertram.

35. Captain Wentworth to Anne Elliot.

36. Catherine Morland.

ANSWERS: LOVE AND MARRIAGE

1. Mr Darcy.

2. Emma Woodhouse.

3. a) Jane and Mr Bingley   b) Lydia and Mr Wickham.

4. b) "Persuasion".

5. Marianne Dashwood.

6. Captain Wentworth.

7. a) Frank Churchill and Jane Fairfax
   b) Harriet Smith and Robert Martin
   c) Mr Elton and Augusta Hawkins.

8. Mrs Bennet, "Pride and Prejudice".

9. a) "Northanger Abbey".

10. c) Charlotte Lucas.

11. Henrietta and Charles Hayter; Louisa and Captain Benwick.

12. Maria Ward marries Sir Thomas Bertram; Miss Ward marries the Rev. Mr Norris; Frances marries Mr Price.

13. Charlotte Lucas.

14. True.

15. Henry Tilney.

16. "Mansfield Park".

17. a) Edward Ferrars   b) Robert Ferrars.

18. Henrietta and Louisa Musgrove and Captain Wentworth.

19. a) Elizabeth Bennet.

ANSWERS: LOVE AND MARRIAGE

20. a) Charlotte Lucas.

21. b) Maria.

22. Harriet Smith.

23. "Pride and Prejudice." Jane Bennet.

24. True.

25. a) Sophia Grey.

26. False. Emma is talking about Mr Knightley.

27. Jane Bennet and Charles Bingley; Elizabeth Bennet and Mr Darcy.

28. c) "Persuasion".

29. Mary Crawford.

30. Emma.

ANSWERS: SISTERS AND BROTHERS

1. b) Five.

2. Jane, Elizabeth, Lydia, Kitty (Catherine) and Mary.

3. The Dashwood sisters - "Sense and Sensibility";
   The Bertram sisters - "Mansfield Park";
   The Musgrove sisters - "Persuasion".

4. Georgiana.

5. Emma.

6. James Morland to Catherine.

ANSWERS: SISTERS AND BROTHERS

7. False. Three.

8. True.

9. Lucy and Anne.

10. "Persuasion".

11. Marianne Dashwood to Elinor.

12. False. "Persuasion".

13. "Sense and Sensibility".

14. True.

15. Two.

16. c) Mary Crawford.

17. a) "Mansfield Park".

18. Caroline and Louisa.

19. Catherine and Isabella.

20. Anne Elliot - Elizabeth and Mary;
    Elinor Dashwood - Marianne and Margaret.

21. Henrietta and Louisa.

22. a) Lydia.

23. b) "Persuasion".

24. "Emma".

25. Robert.

26. True.

27. Fanny Price; Henry Tilney.

1. Emma.

2. True.

3. "Northanger Abbey" and "Persuasion".

4. a) Combe Magna : iii) John Willoughby;
   b) Delaford : i) Colonel Brandon;
   c) Cleveland : ii) The Palmers.

5. c) "Persuasion".

6. Mr Darcy.

7. Lyme.

8. Portsmouth.

9. a) Mr Knightley : Donwell;
   b) Robert Martin : Abbey-Mill-Farm;
   c) Mr and Mrs Weston : Randalls.

10. Lady Catherine de Bourgh.

11. "Northanger Abbey".

12. Anne Elliot.

13. a) Highbury : ii) "Emma"
    b) Uppercross : iii) "Persuasion"
    c) Sotherton : i) "Mansfield Park".

14. c) Weymouth.

15. "Sense and Sensibility".

16. Brighton.

17. a) The Morlands in "Northanger Abbey".

18. "Northanger Abbey".

ANSWERS: SETTINGS

19. Sotherton.
20. c) "Northanger Abbey".
21. True.

ANSWERS: PRIDE AND PREJUDICE

1. Jane is the eldest, Lydia is the youngest.
2. Mrs Bennet.
3. Charlotte Lucas.
4. Cousin.
5. Lady Catherine de Bourgh.
6. Mary.
7. Mrs Philips and Mr Gardiner.
8. a) Lady Lucas.
9. False. George Wickham.
10. Mr Collins and Mr Darcy.
11. b) Sir William Lucas.
12. c) Lady Catherine.
13. c) Miss Bingley.
14. Lady Catherine.
15. Mrs Forster.
16. Mr and Mrs Bennet.

ANSWERS: PRIDE AND PREJUDICE

17. Mr Darcy.

18. False. Elizabeth.

19. Derbyshire.

20. Mrs Reynolds.

21. Catherine (Kitty).

22. Lydia.

23. Mary.

24. False. Mrs Bennet.

25. True.

ANSWERS: EMMA

1. Miss Taylor and Mr Weston.

2. a) Mr Weston.

3. Son.

4. Mr Woodhouse.

5. Miss Taylor, now Mrs Weston.

6. Henry, John, George, Bella and Emma.

7. Mr Elton.

8. Mr Elton.

9. Mis Bates.

10. Niece.

ANSWERS: EMMA

11. False. Harriet Smith.

12. Robert Martin and Mr Elton.

13. Robert Martin.

14. Jane Fairfax.

15. Emma and Mr Elton.

16. Jane Fairfax.

17. Ford's.

18. b) Frank Churchill.

19. True.

20. a) Mrs Elton   b) Mr Knightley   c) Emma

21. False. Mr Knightley.

22. b) Mrs Elton.

23. Frank Churchill.

24. a) Mrs Elton.

25. Mrs Elton.

26. a) George.

27. Mrs Weston.

ANSWERS: SENSE AND SENSIBILITY

1. John.

2. Fanny Dashwood.

3. b) Fanny Dashwood.

4. Sir John Middleton.

5. Sir John and Lady Middleton.

6. True.

7. Mrs Jennings.

8. Mrs Jennings.

9. Marianne. John Willoughby.

10. John Willoughby.

11. Marianne.

12. c) Edward.

13. Sir John talking about Willoughby.

14. Charlotte Palmer.

15. a) Colonel Brandon.

16. Brother.

17. Mr and Mrs Palmer.

18. Sir John and Lady Middleton.

19. Mr Palmer.

20. Lucy Steele.

21. False. Mrs Jennings.

22. Eliza.

ANSWERS: SENSE AND SENSIBILITY

23. John Willoughby.

24. a) Mrs Ferrars.

25. True.

26. John Willoughby.

ANSWERS: PERSUASION

1. Sir Walter Elliot.

2. Lady Russell.

3. Mr Shepherd.

4. Mr Shepherd's.

5. Admiral and Mrs Croft.

6. Sir Walter.

7. c) sister.

8. a) Mrs Clay.

9. A ship.

10. False. Captain Wentworth.

11. Mrs Croft.

12. a) Lady Russell.

13. Captain and Mrs Harville.

14. Walter and Charles.

15. Captain Benwick.

ANSWERS: PERSUASION

16. Fanny. She died.

17. Miss Hamilton, now Mrs Smith.

18. Lady Russell.

19. Sir Walter.

ANSWERS: MANSFIELD PARK

1. Northampton.

2. b) Ten.

3. They are her aunts.

4. True.

5. Tom, Edmund, Maria and Julia.

6. A sailor.

7. Mrs Norris.

8. Edmund and Fanny.

9. Lady Bertram.

10. a) Mr Rushworth.

11. Brother and sister.

12. c) Mrs Norris.

13. Lady Bertram.

14. True.

15. Edmund.

ANSWERS: MANSFIELD PARK

16. c) Mary Crawford.

17. Mrs Norris.

18. True.

19. b) Edmund.

20. Edmund.

21. False. Henry Crawford.

22. She is talking to Sir Thomas about Henry Crawford.

23. Fanny's.

24. Maria. Henry Crawford.

25. Mr Yates.

26. Susan.

27. Dr Grant.

ANSWERS: NORTHANGER ABBEY

1. A clergyman.

2. Richard.

3. Mrs Allen.

4. b) Nine.

5. False. Mrs Allen.

6. Henry Tilney.

7. Clergyman.

ANSWERS: NORTHANGER ABBEY

8. Pulteney Street.

9. They are old school friends.

10. John Thorpe.

11. John Thorpe.

12. True.

13. c) Frederick.

14. Mrs Allen.

15. False. Mrs Thorpe.

16. Henry Tilney to Catherine Morland.

17. b) Isabella.

18. Woodston.

19. Isabella to Catherine

20. a) Henry Tilney.

21. a) Catherine.

22. Isabella.

23. Catherine's.

ANSWERS: DIFFICULT ONES

1. Steventon, Hampshire on 16th December, 1775.

2. The name for works written when Jane Austen was a young girl.

3. Cassandra.

4. In the form of letters.

5. " Susan".

6. Twelve .

7. "Elinor and Marianne".

8. March 1815.

9. Surgeon.

10. "Pride and Prejudice".

11. James.

12. Fifteen.

13. "A History of England".

14. "Sanditon".

15. "Lesley Castle".

16. "Sanditon".

17. Winchester, 18th July 1817.

18. "Northanger Abbey" and "Persuasion".